The Common Sense Fitness Journal

Supercharge Your Motivation and Make Exercise Fun!

Health Balanced Publications
Carmel, NY

Published by Health Balanced Publications
Copyright © 2019 Agi Kadar

Agi@HealthBalanced.com
HealthBalanced.com

ISBN 978-1-7338910-0-4

Dedication

This journal is dedicated to

My husband, Tibor.
Thank you for loving me and supporting
me in everything I do.

Carl Pichotta.
My friend and "brother" who is always there to
inspire and encourage me to do the
best I can in everything.
Thank you for keeping me accountable,
believing in me and cheering me on.

~ Notes ~

~ Disclaimer ~

This book is not intended as a substitute for the medical advice of physicians.

Always check with your doctor before beginning this or any other exercise, nutrition or supplement program.

The opinions and statements in this book are intended for informational use only, They are the author's opinions and are based on her experience.

The information in this book is meant to educate and serve as an aid to the reader's health and well being. They should not be considered as medical advice, diagnoses, or treatment.

The author and publisher of this material do not accept any liability or responsibility for any injury or damage that may occur through following the material and instructions in this book.

The reader should consult a physician before engaging in any of the activities described in this book.

"Though no one can go back and make a brand new start, anyone can start from now and make a brand new ending."

~ Carl Bard ~

The cave you fear to enter holds the treasure you seek.
Joseph Campbell

~ Introduction ~

Would you like to feel better, be stronger,
look younger, and live longer?

Would you like to have more energy to
do more and be more confident?

Do you lack the desire to exercise?
Do you think you couldn't do it?

Are you afraid to join a gym and get intimidated
by heavy weights and fitness equipment?

This journal will give you the simple steps to
find your motivation, get over your fears, defeat
your obstacles, become more confident and
make your goals happen. It will make you see
that fitness doesn't have to be difficult and
that exercise can be fun.

It will show you how to get out of your
comfort zone. Get started and have fun.

~ Move To Live! ~

~ Notes ~

~ Notes ~

How to Use This Journal

This 30 day journal is here to help you to start on your fitness journey and create a habit that will keep you motivated and make exercise an enjoyable part of your life.

By following the instructions and completing the activity pages you will have the foundation for creating a healthy, and active lifestyle.

To support your journey you have been provided with daily journaling pages to give you the opportunity to track your activities and progress.

You will write your goals to inspire and motivate you to take action. You will record your accomplishments to help you change your mindset and reinforce healthy habits. Have fun and think about the positive impact you are creating for your life.

**Do it because you love your body,
not because you hate it!**

How to Use This Journal

Take a few minutes first thing in the morning to write in your journal to set the tone for the day and reinforce your motivation and the consistent habit to be active. Then write again at the end of the day, to track your progress and celebrate your wins.

Consistency is the key to establish habits and positive changes. Writing them down will help you see even the smallest changes in the right direction and will help you stay the course.

Several blank pages are included in the journal for you to write down your thoughts, and insights you discover about yourself and how your positive changes will affect others around you.

Collect inspiring quotes, and pictures. Favorite exercises you learned, obstacles you conquered. Ideas on how you will celebrate your victories.

Respect yourself!
Respect your body!

Do it for you!

~ Notes ~

~ Activity Pages ~

The following activities will help you find your motivation, make a commitment to yourself and get started on your new routine.

Dare to begin!

Take the next step!

Create a habit!

~ Notes ~

~ My Commitment ~

I _____
make a commitment to start exercising and write in this journal every morning and every evening to track my progress, feelings and accomplishments.

Physical activity is important to me, because I am important to me.

I respect myself, I respect my body and want to treat it well.

I will refer back to this contract and my goals and dreams when I feel like making excuses not to be active.

_____
Signature

_____
Date

~ My Dreams ~

Directions: Answer the following questions. Reflect on your answers. Dare to dream!

What is my heartfelt dream?_____

_____

_____

_____

What will my life be like when I fulfill my dream?

_____

_____

_____

How can a more active lifestyle help me to achieve my dream?

_____

_____

_____

~ Finding My Why ~

Getting clear on your "why" will give you the motivation and inspiration you need to start.

Directions: Answer the following questions. Think beyond health, losing weight and getting in shape.

Why is exercise important to me? What can it do for me?

_____

_____

_____

What can the results of an active lifestyle can do for me? _____

_____

_____

What can being stronger and more confident with more energy can do for me?

_____

_____

_____

~ Setting My Goals ~

Keeping your goals front of you will help you keep going when you don't feel like it.

Take the Next Step!

What goals can I set to motivate me to exercise?

_____

_____

_____

What will make me like the person in the mirror?

_____

_____

_____

How do I want to feel? (Mind and body.)

_____

_____

_____

~ Recognizing Obstacles ~

Do It Anyway!

What is stopping me from exercising?

_____

_____

_____

What am I afraid of?

_____

_____

_____

Who can I count on for support when I am
looking for excuses?

_____

_____

_____

~ My Thoughts ~

Resources to Help
You Get Started

Go to GetFitGift.com to download a free
chapter on "Finding Your Why?
From Agi Kadar's book: *Are You a Gym Mouse?*

Read the book by Agi Kadar:
Are You a Gym Mouse?

Email Agi any questions you have and
find out about personal coaching:
Agi@HealthBalanced.com

~ Notes ~

~ My Personal Reasons ~

Directions: Check all the things that are important to you on the next page. Highlight the three most important reasons that will get you started.

Refer back to this list when you find yourself making excuses not to work out.

Add your own ideas on the following pages.

Keep these questions in mind:

What can being active do for me?

What will motivate me to exercise daily?

How my positive changes will affect my life and others around me?

~ My "Why" Checklist ~

- ☐ Health
- ☐ Strength, Better Shape
- ☐ Looking Better and Younger
- ☐ Feeling Better
- ☐ Having More Energy
- ☐ Having More Confidence
- ☐ Better Self-Esteem
- ☐ Less Pain
- ☐ More Mobility, Flexibility
- ☐ Losing Weight
- ☐ Gaining Muscle
- ☐ Having More Endurance
- ☐ Living Longer and Better
- ☐ Feeling Better in My Skin
- ☐ Feeling Better in My Clothes
- ☐ Keeping Up with My Spouse
- ☐ Keeping Up with My Children
- ☐ Keeping Up with My Grandchildren
- ☐ Keeping Up with My Friends
- ☐ Loving Myself More

~ My "Why" Checklist ~

- ☐ Being More Comfortable with People
- ☐ Socializing
- ☐ Going out
- ☐ Dancing
- ☐ Dating
- ☐ Entertaining
- ☐ Getting a Better Job
- ☐ Taking Exercise Classes
- ☐ Meeting New People
- ☐ Walking, Running Races
- ☐ Hiking, Climbing
- ☐ Skiing, Ice Skating
- ☐ Active Vacations
- ☐ Biking Tours
- ☐ Wearing a Bathing Suit
- ☐ Going to the Beach / Pool
- ☐ Swimming
- ☐ Playing Sports
- ☐ Camping

My Personal Inspirations

☐ _____

☐ _____

☐ _____

☐ _____

☐ _____

☐ _____

☐ _____

☐ _____

☐ _____

☐ _____

☐ _____

☐ _____

☐ _____

☐ _____

☐ _____

☐ _____

☐ _____

My Personal Inspirations

- ☐ _____
- ☐ _____
- ☐ _____
- ☐ _____
- ☐ _____
- ☐ _____
- ☐ _____
- ☐ _____
- ☐ _____
- ☐ _____
- ☐ _____
- ☐ _____
- ☐ _____
- ☐ _____
- ☐ _____
- ☐ _____
- ☐ _____
- ☐ _____

~ Getting Started~

Don't wait! There will never be a better time to start than right now! So make the time to do it, make it fun and stick with it!

Don't make fitness a chore. Find exercises you like, and are comfortable with. You will be more likely to do it.

List some indoor activities you enjoy:

_____

_____

_____

_____

List some outdoor activities you like:

_____

_____

_____

Start out with a few minutes a day and increase the duration and intensity of your sessions

~ Keep Going ~

Commit to 15-30 minutes of
movement every day.

Vary your activities!

- ☐ Go for a walk

- ☐ Go for a bike ride

- ☐ Dust off your home exercise equipment
  and start using it

- ☐ Dance around to your favorite music

- ☐ Join a gym and make an appointment
  for an orientation session to get to know
  the place

- ☐ Hire a personal trainer

- ☐ Try different exercise classes for variety,
  comradery, direction and support

- ☐ Find an exercise buddy

My ideas:

_____

_____

_____

My Inspirational Quotes

My Inspirational Pictures

Find some motivational pictures of activities, exercises you like and people who inspire you and paste them here.

My Inspirational Pictures

Create a vision board.
Make some drawings.

My Inspirational Pictures

Start a binder for fitness articles,
pictures and ideas.

~ Notes ~

Your 30 Day Activity Journal

Start Small
Start Simple
Start Now

Date:_____ Day 1

Morning

What will motivate me to exercise today?

_____

_____

_____

How do I want to feel? Mind and body.

_____

_____

_____

What activity will I do today and where?

_____

_____

_____

Day: _____

Evening

What amazing things did I accomplish today?

_____

_____

_____

How do I feel? Mind and body.

_____

_____

_____

What will I focus on tomorrow?

_____

_____

_____

Date:_____   Day 2

Morning

What will motivate me to exercise today?

_____

_____

_____

How do I want to feel? Mind and body.

_____

_____

_____

What activity will I do today and where?

_____

_____

_____

Day: _____

Evening

What amazing things did I accomplish today?

_____

_____

_____

How do I feel? Mind and body.

_____

_____

_____

What will I focus on tomorrow?

_____

_____

_____

Date:_____ Day 3

Morning

What will motivate me to exercise today?

_____

_____

_____

How do I want to feel? Mind and body.

_____

_____

_____

What activity will I do today and where?

_____

_____

_____

Day: _____

Evening

What amazing things did I accomplish today?

_____
_____
_____

How do I feel? Mind and body.

_____
_____
_____

What will I focus on tomorrow?

_____
_____
_____

Date:_____ Day 4

Morning

What will motivate me to exercise today?

_____

_____

_____

How do I want to feel? Mind and body.

_____

_____

_____

What activity will I do today and where?

_____

_____

_____

Day: _____

Evening

What amazing things did I accomplish today?

_____
_____
_____

How do I feel? Mind and body.

_____
_____
_____

What will I focus on tomorrow?

_____
_____
_____

Date:_____ Day 5

Morning

What will motivate me to exercise today?

_____

_____

_____

How do I want to feel? Mind and body.

_____

_____

_____

What activity will I do today and where?

_____

_____

_____

Day: _____

Evening

What amazing things did I accomplish today?

_____
_____
_____

How do I feel? Mind and body.

_____
_____
_____

What will I focus on tomorrow?

_____
_____
_____

Date:_____ Day 6

Morning

What will motivate me to exercise today?

_____

_____

_____

How do I want to feel? Mind and body.

_____

_____

_____

What activity will I do today and where?

_____

_____

_____

Day: _____

Evening

What amazing things did I accomplish today?

_____

_____

_____

How do I feel? Mind and body.

_____

_____

_____

What will I focus on tomorrow?

_____

_____

_____

Date:_____ Day 7

Morning

What will motivate me to exercise today?

_____
_____
_____

How do I want to feel? Mind and body.

_____
_____
_____

What activity will I do today and where?

_____
_____
_____

Day: _____

Evening

What amazing things did I accomplish today?

_____

_____

_____

How do I feel? Mind and body.

_____

_____

_____

What will I focus on tomorrow?

_____

_____

_____

Date:_____ Day 8

Morning

What will motivate me to exercise today?

_____

_____

_____

How do I want to feel? Mind and body.

_____

_____

_____

What activity will I do today and where?

_____

_____

_____

Day: _____

Evening

What amazing things did I accomplish today?

_____
_____
_____

How do I feel? Mind and body.

_____
_____
_____

What will I focus on tomorrow?

_____
_____
_____

Date:_____ Day 9

Morning

What will motivate me to exercise today?

_____

_____

_____

How do I want to feel? Mind and body.

_____

_____

_____

What activity will I do today and where?

_____

_____

_____

Day: _____

Evening

What amazing things did I accomplish today?

_____

_____

_____

How do I feel? Mind and body.

_____

_____

_____

What will I focus on tomorrow?

_____

_____

_____

Date:_____ Day 10

Morning

What will motivate me to exercise today?

_____

_____

_____

How do I want to feel? Mind and body.

_____

_____

_____

What activity will I do today and where?

_____

_____

_____

Day: _____

Evening

What amazing things did I accomplish today?

_____

_____

_____

How do I feel? Mind and body.

_____

_____

_____

What will I focus on tomorrow?

_____

_____

_____

Date:_____ Day 11

Morning

What will motivate me to exercise today?

_____

_____

_____

How do I want to feel? Mind and body.

_____

_____

_____

What activity will I do today and where?

_____

_____

_____

Day: _____

Evening

What amazing things did I accomplish today?

_____

_____

_____

How do I feel? Mind and body.

_____

_____

_____

What will I focus on tomorrow?

_____

_____

_____

Date:_____ Day 12

Morning

What will motivate me to exercise today?

_____

_____

_____

How do I want to feel? Mind and body.

_____

_____

_____

What activity will I do today and where?

_____

_____

_____

Day: _____

Evening

What amazing things did I accomplish today?

_____

_____

_____

How do I feel? Mind and body.

_____

_____

_____

What will I focus on tomorrow?

_____

_____

_____

Date:_____ Day 13

Morning

What will motivate me to exercise today?

_____

_____

_____

How do I want to feel? Mind and body.

_____

_____

_____

What activity will I do today and where?

_____

_____

_____

Day: _____

Evening

What amazing things did I accomplish today?

_____
_____
_____

How do I feel? Mind and body.

_____
_____
_____

What will I focus on tomorrow?

_____
_____
_____

Date:_____ Day 14

Morning

What will motivate me to exercise today?

_____

_____

_____

How do I want to feel? Mind and body.

_____

_____

_____

What activity will I do today and where?

_____

_____

_____

Day: _____

Evening

What amazing things did I accomplish today?

_____

_____

_____

How do I feel? Mind and body.

_____

_____

_____

What will I focus on tomorrow?

_____

_____

_____

Date:_____ Day 15

Morning

What will motivate me to exercise today?

_____

_____

_____

How do I want to feel? Mind and body.

_____

_____

_____

What activity will I do today and where?

_____

_____

_____

Day: _____

Evening

What amazing things did I accomplish today?

_____

_____

_____

How do I feel? Mind and body.

_____

_____

_____

What will I focus on tomorrow?

_____

_____

_____

Date:_____ Day 16

Morning

What will motivate me to exercise today?

_____

_____

_____

How do I want to feel? Mind and body.

_____

_____

_____

What activity will I do today and where?

_____

_____

_____

Day: _____

Evening

What amazing things did I accomplish today?

_____

_____

_____

How do I feel? Mind and body.

_____

_____

_____

What will I focus on tomorrow?

_____

_____

_____

Date:_____ Day 17

Morning

What will motivate me to exercise today?

_____

_____

_____

How do I want to feel? Mind and body.

_____

_____

_____

What activity will I do today and where?

_____

_____

_____

Day: _____

Evening

What amazing things did I accomplish today?

_____
_____
_____

How do I feel? Mind and body.

_____
_____
_____

What will I focus on tomorrow?

_____
_____
_____

Date:_____   Day 18

Morning

What will motivate me to exercise today?

_____

_____

_____

How do I want to feel? Mind and body.

_____

_____

_____

What activity will I do today and where?

_____

_____

_____

Day: _____

Evening

What amazing things did I accomplish today?

_____

_____

_____

How do I feel? Mind and body.

_____

_____

_____

What will I focus on tomorrow?

_____

_____

_____

Date:_____ Day 19

Morning

What will motivate me to exercise today?

_____

_____

_____

How do I want to feel? Mind and body.

_____

_____

_____

What activity will I do today and where?

_____

_____

_____

Day: _____

Evening

What amazing things did I accomplish today?

_____

_____

_____

How do I feel? Mind and body.

_____

_____

_____

What will I focus on tomorrow?

_____

_____

_____

Date:_____ Day 20

Morning

What will motivate me to exercise today?

_____

_____

_____

How do I want to feel? Mind and body.

_____

_____

_____

What activity will I do today and where?

_____

_____

_____

Day: _____

Evening

What amazing things did I accomplish today?

_____

_____

_____

How do I feel? Mind and body.

_____

_____

_____

What will I focus on tomorrow?

_____

_____

_____

Date:_____ Day 21

Morning

What will motivate me to exercise today?

_____

_____

_____

How do I want to feel? Mind and body.

_____

_____

_____

What activity will I do today and where?

_____

_____

_____

Day: _____

Evening

What amazing things did I accomplish today?

_____

_____

_____

How do I feel? Mind and body.

_____

_____

_____

What will I focus on tomorrow?

_____

_____

_____

Date:_____ Day 22

Morning

What will motivate me to exercise today?

_____

_____

_____

How do I want to feel? Mind and body.

_____

_____

_____

What activity will I do today and where?

_____

_____

_____

Day: _____

Evening

What amazing things did I accomplish today?

_____

_____

_____

How do I feel? Mind and body.

_____

_____

_____

What will I focus on tomorrow?

_____

_____

_____

Date:_____   Day 23

Morning

What will motivate me to exercise today?

_____

_____

_____

How do I want to feel? Mind and body.

_____

_____

_____

What activity will I do today and where?

_____

_____

_____

Day: _____

Evening

What amazing things did I accomplish today?

_____

_____

_____

How do I feel? Mind and body.

_____

_____

_____

What will I focus on tomorrow?

_____

_____

_____

Date:_____ Day 24

Morning

What will motivate me to exercise today?

_____

_____

_____

How do I want to feel? Mind and body.

_____

_____

_____

What activity will I do today and where?

_____

_____

_____

Day: _____

Evening

What amazing things did I accomplish today?

_____

_____

_____

How do I feel? Mind and body.

_____

_____

_____

What will I focus on tomorrow?

_____

_____

_____

Date:_____ Day 25

Morning

What will motivate me to exercise today?

_____

_____

_____

How do I want to feel? Mind and body.

_____

_____

_____

What activity will I do today and where?

_____

_____

_____

Day: _____

Evening

What amazing things did I accomplish today?

_____
_____
_____

How do I feel? Mind and body.

_____
_____
_____

What will I focus on tomorrow?

_____
_____
_____

Date:_____ Day 26

Morning

What will motivate me to exercise today?

_____

_____

_____

How do I want to feel? Mind and body.

_____

_____

_____

What activity will I do today and where?

_____

_____

_____

Day: _____

Evening

What amazing things did I accomplish today?

_____

_____

_____

How do I feel? Mind and body.

_____

_____

_____

What will I focus on tomorrow?

_____

_____

_____

Date:_____ Day 27

Morning

What will motivate me to exercise today?

_____

_____

_____

How do I want to feel? Mind and body.

_____

_____

_____

What activity will I do today and where?

_____

_____

_____

Day: _____

Evening

What amazing things did I accomplish today?

_____
_____
_____

How do I feel? Mind and body.

_____
_____
_____

What will I focus on tomorrow?

_____
_____
_____

Date:_____ Day 28

Morning

What will motivate me to exercise today?

_____

_____

_____

How do I want to feel? Mind and body.

_____

_____

_____

What activity will I do today and where?

_____

_____

_____

Day: _____

Evening

What amazing things did I accomplish today?

_____

_____

_____

How do I feel? Mind and body.

_____

_____

_____

What will I focus on tomorrow?

_____

_____

_____

Date:_____ **Day 29**

Morning

What will motivate me to exercise today?

_____

_____

_____

How do I want to feel? Mind and body.

_____

_____

_____

What activity will I do today and where?

_____

_____

_____

Day: _____

Evening

What amazing things did I accomplish today?

_____

_____

_____

How do I feel? Mind and body.

_____

_____

_____

What will I focus on tomorrow?

_____

_____

_____

Date:_____ Day 30

Morning

What will motivate me to exercise today?

_____

_____

_____

How do I want to feel? Mind and body.

_____

_____

_____

What activity will I do today and where?

_____

_____

_____

Day: _____

Evening

What amazing things did I accomplish today?

_____

_____

_____

How do I feel? Mind and body.

_____

_____

_____

What will I focus on tomorrow?

_____

_____

_____

~ Notes ~

~ Keep Moving ~

"We are what we repeatedly do.
Excellence then is not an act, but a habit"
~ Aristotle ~

Don't let your momentum stop or slow down.

You came this far, you created a habit.

Start another journal or contact Agi for ideas,
personal coaching, online classes, courses,
books and more support.

~ Time for Reflection ~

What are your thoughts on being active every day?

_____

_____

What do you know now that you didn't know 30 days ago?

_____

_____

What was the most meaningful goal that you have achieved in the past 30 days?

_____

_____

What have you learned about yourself?

_____

_____

What are you most grateful for?

_____

_____

~ Time for Reflection ~

What activities do you enjoy most?

_____

_____

What activities would you like to try in the future?

_____

_____

What will help you to continue exercising every day?

_____

_____

What obstacles are you still working on defeating?

_____

_____

How will you change your goals for the future?

_____

_____

~ Notes ~

~ Next Steps ~

Motivation is what got you started.
Commitment is what will keep you going.

Now that you've created an exercise habit, what will you do to keep your momentum going?

_____

_____

_____

_____

How will you celebrate your accomplishments?

_____

_____

_____

_____

Start another journal.
Read my book: *Are You a Gym Mouse?*
Find out about online classes, personal
coaching and accountability options.

Contact Me to Discuss Your Next Steps
Agi Kadar
Agi@HealthBalanced.com

~ About the Author ~

Agi Kadar is a NASM Certified Personal Trainer and a Holistic Lifestyle Coach. She has been working with people of all ages and abilities for over 20 years, one on one and in groups.

She specializes in motivating and inspiring them to move for life. Showing them that an active life can be doable and enjoyable for everyone, regardless of age and physical abilities.

Agi's book, *Are You a Gym Mouse?* received recognition as a finalist at the "Author Academy Awards" and won second place in the "Reader's Choice Awards" in 2018

If you found this journal helpful, please leave a review on Amazon.com

~ More Resources ~

To receive a free downloadable gift and a
chapter of Agi's book, and to sign up for
information on upcoming publications, classes,
and courses go to: GetFitGift.com

You can find Agi's work at:
amazon.com/author/agikadar
HealthBalanced.com
Email: Agi@HealthBalanced.com

Look for more books, journals and classes
being published later this year.

40682982R00060

Made in the USA
Middletown, DE
29 March 2019